God's Promise to a Child of Divorce

You are Held

Written by Anna Locke

Illustrations by Beth Snider

Deeply Rooted Publications

DeeplyRootedPublications.com

I dedicate this book to my mother, Sybil.
Your love for people has always been an inspiration to me.
You persevered through many difficult seasons in your life.
Yet you did what it took, working tirelessly to raise me.
Thank you for being my mama!

Edited by Deborah K. Frontiera, *www.authorsden.com/deborahkfrontiera*
Design by Monica Thomas for TLC Book Design, *TLCBookDesign.com*
Illustrated by Beth Snider, *BethSniderArt.com*

Mama sits on the side of my bed to tuck me in every night, weaving a story into my ears.

"Jo Jo the koala bear sat high up in the eucalyptus tree. He loved looking out from his tree and eating eucalyptus leaves all day. But on this day, he felt alone, so he climbed down and set out to find his family."

As the words fall from her mouth, I think about my family.
Daddy doesn't live with us anymore. I see him on weekends and
holidays, and sometimes in a dream where we are all together again.

Mama finishes the story and we fold our hands to pray. Then she tucks me in tight and kisses me goodnight. After she slips out of the room, I close my eyes to talk to God some more.

"Dear God, I feel alone and lost. Where is my family?"

I wait. I can hear my own heartbeat. I am listening with my ears, but His voice speaks to my heart, so very different from my own thoughts which are more like swirling wind.

My child, I have searched for you like treasure.
I know you. You are not lost but found.
You are not alone, but chosen.

I know when you sit, when you rise up,
and even what you think about.

I know when you go out or when you are lying down.

Even when you feel as far away as the far side of the sea,
I am with you. I go before you, and I protect you from behind.
My hand will guide you; My right hand will hold onto you.

You are held.

*Even when you think the darkness has hidden you and
made you invisible, it is not dark to me, for darkness is
as light to me. I see you even when you feel unseen.*

I know you have many questions.

*I created you to ask and to wonder. I formed your inmost
being. You are fearfully and wonderfully made! Nothing
about you was hidden when I made you in the secret place.
I am the author of the story of your life.*

You are held.

Your family has been right here all along. Families come in all shapes and sizes.

I know you wonder why your daddy had to leave. You wonder why you have to watch him drive away after every weekend visit. You wonder if he remembers you when he is away. A story cannot be understood on a single page. You are so loved. Your mama and daddy think about you wherever they go, and my thoughts for you outnumber the grains of sand.

I awake with a start.
Mama is here sitting
on the side of my bed.
She heard me cry out
in my sleep.

"I hate all the hurt!"

My anger feels hot like fire in my heart.

Mama's words are soft. "When your daddy is away, he is still your daddy. And you have a Father in heaven, who is always with you. He is a Father even to the fatherless. Anger can reveal a place we need God to heal. It is a signal He can use to light the way to hope. Sometimes I am angry, too."

"You are?" I ask.
Somehow, I feel less alone.

I push back the tears, so Mama won't see me cry.
But she sees them. I see hers, too.

Mama traces the scar on my elbow with her finger
as she talks to me. I got that scar when I fell off my
swing in the backyard. Mama had bandaged me up.
We laugh as we remember how I had done a
back flip on the way to the ground.

"Laughing tastes sweet through our tears,"
mama says, "just as the sunshine is always
brightest after the rain. We feel scars in deeper
places, too, the ones that no one else
can see."

Then I remember all the messes I made—
a broken dish, my toys left on the living room
rug, my wet towel on the bathroom floor.

"Maybe it's my fault."

Mama looks at me deeply.

"NO, my love. You are not to blame.
You are just who you were meant
to be. Sometimes things happen
that don't seem to make sense.
We are all learning how to love.
You are a gift. Messes are memories
in the making."

"God has set you on this path. Sometimes the way will seem easy. Other times the way may be crooked and rocky. But God's hand will guide you. One day, you can show someone else the way."

"God's own Son, Jesus, once had to walk a dark road to a cross where He stretched out His arms, and He took on the hurt of the whole world. He gave His life for you, Little One, to open the way to the Father! One day He will come again to fix all that is broken. Then the only scars you will see are the scars of perfect love on His feet and hands.

In these hands,
you are held."

"Search me, O God, and know my heart;
test me and know my anxious thoughts.

See if there is any way of pain, grief, or sorrow in me,
and lead me in the way everlasting."

Psalm 139 (NIV)

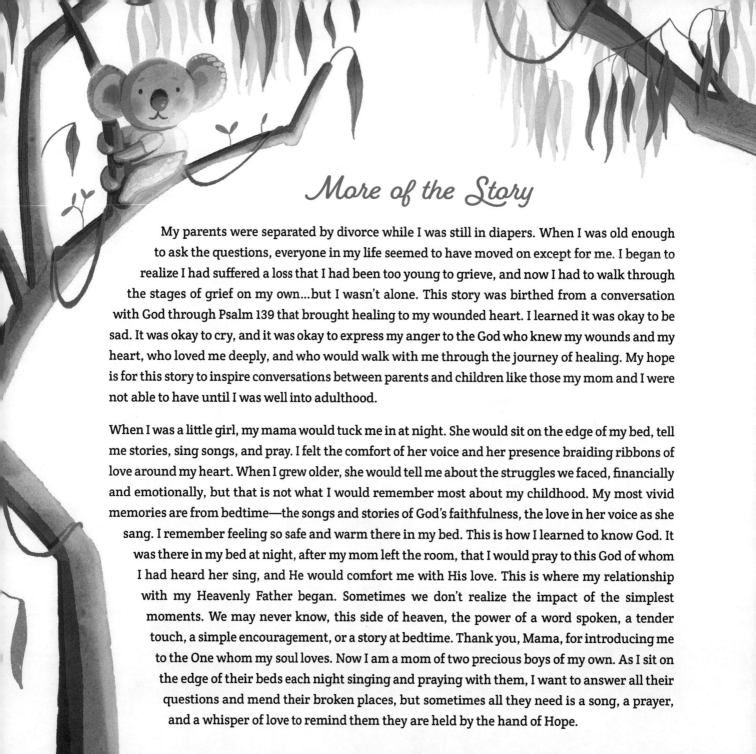

More of the Story

My parents were separated by divorce while I was still in diapers. When I was old enough to ask the questions, everyone in my life seemed to have moved on except for me. I began to realize I had suffered a loss that I had been too young to grieve, and now I had to walk through the stages of grief on my own...but I wasn't alone. This story was birthed from a conversation with God through Psalm 139 that brought healing to my wounded heart. I learned it was okay to be sad. It was okay to cry, and it was okay to express my anger to the God who knew my wounds and my heart, who loved me deeply, and who would walk with me through the journey of healing. My hope is for this story to inspire conversations between parents and children like those my mom and I were not able to have until I was well into adulthood.

When I was a little girl, my mama would tuck me in at night. She would sit on the edge of my bed, tell me stories, sing songs, and pray. I felt the comfort of her voice and her presence braiding ribbons of love around my heart. When I grew older, she would tell me about the struggles we faced, financially and emotionally, but that is not what I would remember most about my childhood. My most vivid memories are from bedtime—the songs and stories of God's faithfulness, the love in her voice as she sang. I remember feeling so safe and warm there in my bed. This is how I learned to know God. It was there in my bed at night, after my mom left the room, that I would pray to this God of whom I had heard her sing, and He would comfort me with His love. This is where my relationship with my Heavenly Father began. Sometimes we don't realize the impact of the simplest moments. We may never know, this side of heaven, the power of a word spoken, a tender touch, a simple encouragement, or a story at bedtime. Thank you, Mama, for introducing me to the One whom my soul loves. Now I am a mom of two precious boys of my own. As I sit on the edge of their beds each night singing and praying with them, I want to answer all their questions and mend their broken places, but sometimes all they need is a song, a prayer, and a whisper of love to remind them they are held by the hand of Hope.

Thoughts for talking with our children

1. **It's okay to ask questions.** Asking questions is how we seek and gain understanding. Asking questions about God grows our faith. He welcomes our questions and delights in our curiosity (Hebrews 4:16). As a good Father, he hears us, comforts us, and leads us into greater understanding as we are ready to receive it. We can make room for our children to ask questions as we pray for wisdom to respond to them appropriately. We can be honest with them without revealing things their hearts are not ready to process. God does not answer all of our questions. Instead, He leads us to remember who He is and all He has done (Proverbs 3:5–6).

2. **It's okay to be angry.** Our hearts long for heaven where all things are made right. When we experience the brokenness of this life, it is normal to feel anger. In order to process the emotions of grief, we must be given permission to express them safely (Ephesians 4:26–27). Allowing our children (and ourselves) to vent and lament is part of the healing process, but we do not want to dwell there. We should always seek the Peace of God and direct our children to find their hope in Him (John 14:27). Depending on the age of the child, they may not be able to tell you how they are feeling and may express their emotions through actions. We can prayerfully seek to discern the emotions behind their actions and to respond with understanding.

3. **It's okay to cry.** It may hurt us to see our children cry. Yet, our tears can be a healing balm to the soul (Psalm 56:8), and laughter is never sweeter than when it comes on the heels of a good cry. Oh, the intimacy that blossoms from crying together with our child as we remember we are held in the arms of our Heavenly Father.

4. **It's okay to trust Him.** God is for you and for your child. No matter what we experience in this life, we can take heart that God is good (John 16:33). He is always and forever will be working all things for the good of those who love him (Romans 8:28). He will bring beauty from the ashes (Isaiah 61:3). His hand will guide you; His right hand will hold you fast (Psalm 139:10).

About the Author & Illustrator

Anna Locke has a heart to testify to the love of Jesus and the Gospel of God's grace. She has served as an elementary school teacher for 20 years and has a desire to foster a love of reading and teach her students how to write their own stories. She and her husband Kris are co-founders of Deeply Rooted Marriage Ministry. Anna was born and raised in South Carolina where they live with their two sons and miniature long-haired dachshund named Jackson.

Beth Snider is an illustrator from the Kansas City area where she lives with her husband who is an elementary school teacher and a Youtuber with an outdoor adventure channel. They have three sons, a daughter and an award-winning black lab dog named Georgie. She enjoys creating delicious meals in the kitchen for her family and baking bread. When she's not illustrating, you can find her on the couch, braiding her daughter's hair, cup of coffee nearby, watching an episode of *Little House on the Prairie*.

Printed in the USA
CPSIA information can be obtained
at www.ICGtesting.com
LVHW071119291124
797948LV00015B/38